THE BLOCK ESTATE
10:49 P.M.
AUGUST 31ST

W9-BWW-327

MASSIE, IT'S REALLY VERY SIMPLE—YOU'RE NOT GOING.

MISSING OUT TOMORROW COULD STUNT MY SOCIAL GROWTH FOR THE REST OF THE YEAR.

PLAN
SEP 1ST
10 A.M. SPA
12 A.M. LUNCH
          (SUSHI)
2 P.M. SHOPPING♥
5 P.M.   TEA TIME
6 P.M.   H

EVERYONE WILL HAVE A FRESH BATCH OF INSIDE JOKES I WON'T EVEN GET!

AND YOU KNOW DYLAN WILL BUY THE YSL LIP MARKERS I PUT A "YES" STICKER ON IN *LUCKY.*

JUST SO I CAN MEET SOME GIRL FROM ORLANDO WHO'S GOING TO BE LIVING HERE FOR A YEAR!

I MEAN, WHAT'S THE URGENCY? SHE'S NOT GOING ANYWHERE.

UNLESS OF COURSE SHE HAS A LIFE-THREATENING ILLNESS.

AND IF SHE DOES...

...WHY SHOULD I GET ATTACHED?

9

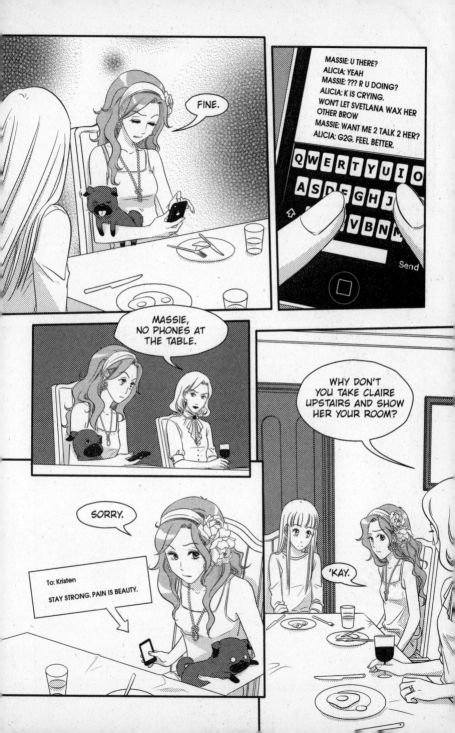

THE BLOCK ESTATE
MASSIE'S BEDROOM
2:25 P.M.
SEPTEMBER 1ST

I HEARD WEST CHESTER IS LIKE THE BEVERLY HILLS OF NEW YORK.

WHAT'S "WEST CHESTER"?

OH, WAIT, YOU MEAN WESTCHESTER?

YEAH, ISN'T THAT WHAT I SAID?

THE BLOCK ESTATE
THE DRIVEWAY
4:15 P.M.
SEPTEMBER 1ST

I CAN'T BELIEVE THAT FAMILY IS TAKING ADVANTAGE OF DADDY LIKE THAT.

WHAT'S SO HARD ABOUT BUYING A HOUSE? ARE THEY POOR, ISAAC?

CLAIRE SEEMS REALLY SWEET. DON'T YOU THINK?

NO. BUT NOT EVERYONE CAN AFFORD EVERYTHING THEY WANT, EXACTLY WHEN THEY WANT IT.

IF I WANTED SOMEONE SWEET FOLLOWING ME AROUND ALL DAY, I'D BRING BEAN.

BE NICE, MASSIE.

VROOM

24

YOU'RE ON A PRIVATE TRAIL.

FUNNY, IT DOESN'T FEEL VERY PRIVATE.

IT WOULD BE IF YOU LEFT.

IS THAT ANY WAY TO TREAT A GUY WHO JUST GOT BACK INTO TOWN?

WHAT WERE YOU IN JAIL FOR?

RECKLESS RIDING.

ACTUALLY, I WAS SHIPPED OFF TO BOARDING SCHOOL IN LONDON, BUT MY DAD MADE ME COME HOME WHEN HE FOUND OUT I WAS PARTYING TOO MUCH.

I GUESS HE'S HOPING I'LL FIND TOTAL MISERY THIS YEAR AS A BRIARWOOD ACADEMY FRESHMAN.

THE GUESTHOUSE
KITCHEN
7:20 A.M.
SEPTEMBER 2ND

AMMO. RAISINS ARE GREAT TO THROW AT PEOPLE IN CLASS.

EWWW, TODD, WHAT WAS THAT?

WANT SOME? MAYBE YOU COULD THROW A FEW AT MASSIE.

I'M SURE YOU'LL BE REALLY POPULAR.

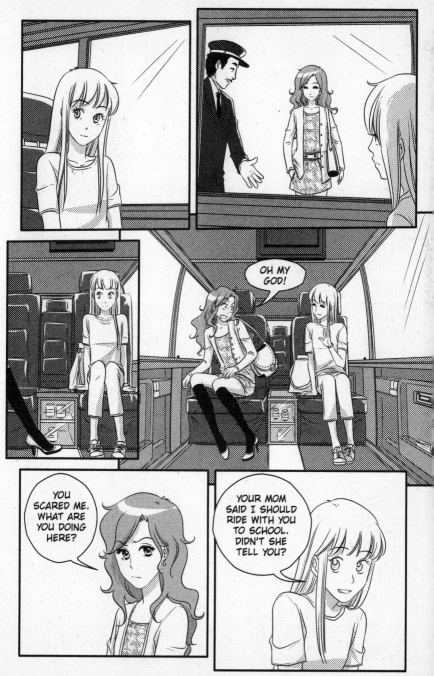

OH MY GOD!

YOU SCARED ME. WHAT ARE YOU DOING HERE?

YOUR MOM SAID I SHOULD RIDE WITH YOU TO SCHOOL. DIDN'T SHE TELL YOU?

CLAIRE, THIS ISN'T EPCOT.

IF THE GUARDS KNOW YOU'RE TAKING PICTURES OF THE HOUSE, THEY'LL CONFISCATE YOUR CAMERA AND QUESTION YOU FOR A WEEK STRAIGHT.

OH MY GOD. I'M SORRY. I'VE NEVER SEEN ANY- THING—

WELL, EVERYONE LIVES LIKE THIS AROUND HERE, SO YOU BETTER GET USED TO IT.

SHE'S IN VINTAGE RALPH LAUREN AND HAS THE NEW PRADA MESSENGER BAG.

WHAT?

'KAY, BE AT YOUR HOUSE IN FIVE MINUTES. BYE.

EHMAGOD, YOU DON'T LOOK LIKE YOU WERE SICK AT ALL. YOU LOOK AH-MAZING!

HEEEYYYY.

41

HEYYY...

WE MISSED YOU YESTERDAY, MASS.

FINALLY SOMEONE WHO LOOKS NICE.

43

47

THE RANGER ROVER
OCTAVIAN COUNTRY DAY SCHOOL
8:27 A.M.
SEPTEMBER 2ND

EXCUSE ME, GUYS, BUT CAN YOU TELL ME HOW TO FIND MY CLASSES?

WHEN YOU GET INSIDE, YOU'LL SEE ROWS OF KIOSKS THAT LOOK LIKE ATM MACHINES.

PUT IN YOUR STUDENT ID CARD AND YOUR SCHEDULE WILL POP OUT.

THE CAFE IS TO THE LEFT ALONG WITH THE GYM, THE DANCE STUDIOS, THE POOL, AND THE SPA.

ON YOUR RIGHT ARE THE SEVENTH-GRADE CLASSROOMS AND THE TEACHERS' LOUNGE.

THANK YOU.

MEET US HERE AT EXACTLY 3:25 IF YOU WANT A RIDE HOME.

IF YOU'RE NOT HERE, WE'LL ASSUME YOU DECIDED TO WALK.

HEY, MASSIE, I HEARD THAT YOU'RE TAKING THAT NEW GIRL UNDER YOUR WING.

WHAT?

YEAH, EVERYONE'S SAYING YOU HAVE A NEW BFF.

I WAS HOPING I COULD MEET HER. IT'S BEEN A WHILE SINCE WE'VE HAD A REAL "FASHION DON'T" AROUND HERE. BUT IF ANYONE CAN WHIP HER INTO SHAPE, YOU CAN.

CHECK YOUR SOURCE, JENA. OBVIOUSLY, IF I HAD A NEW BFF, SHE'D BE HERE RIGHT NOW.

I HEARD SHE PEED IN HER BED AT SLEEPOVER CAMP THIS SUMMER.

TWO GOSSIP POINTS.

56

SORRY, I'M LATE.

AND YOU ARRRRE?

I'M CLAIRE.

HELLO, CLAIRE. I'M VINCENT.

MY LIKES ARE SWING DANCING AND MUST-SEE TV. MY DISLIKES ARE... LET ME THINK... OH, I KNOW...

TARDI-NESS!!

SO IF YOU WOULD PLEASE JUST GRAB A SEAT THERE, I WOULD GREATLY APPRECIATE IT.

YOU HAVE EXACTLY FIFTEEN MINUTES TO PAINT A STILL LIFE CALLED "RIPE VINE TOMATOES."

NOW BEGIN.

CAN I BORROW SOME OF YOUR RED? MINE'S A LITTLE CLUMPY.

SURE.

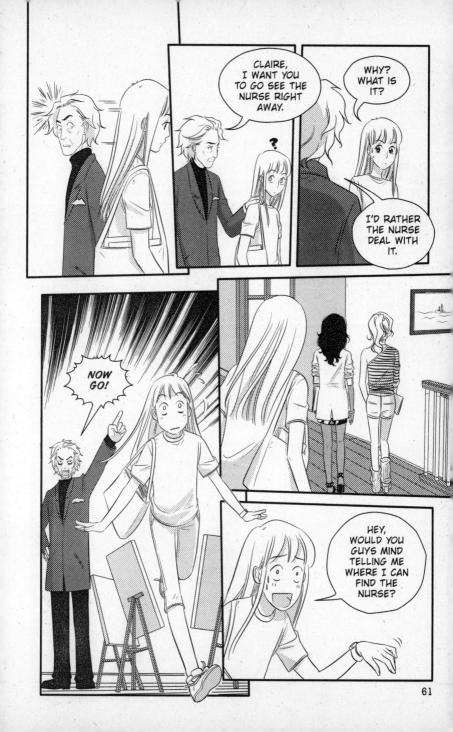

CLAIRE, I WANT YOU TO GO SEE THE NURSE RIGHT AWAY.

WHY? WHAT IS IT?

I'D RATHER THE NURSE DEAL WITH IT.

NOW GO!

HEY, WOULD YOU GUYS MIND TELLING ME WHERE I CAN FIND THE NURSE?

61

64

THIS IS OUR LOST AND FOUND. EVERYTHING HAS BEEN DRY-CLEANED.

GO THROUGH AND PICK OUT SOMETHING YOU LIKE.

SERIOUSLY?

YEAH, WHY NOT? THE GIRLS HERE HARDLY GO LOOKING FOR LAST YEAR'S CLOTHES.

TAKE AS MUCH AS YOU WANT.

REALLY?

I WOULD HAVE TO SAVE FOR YEARS TO AFFORD ONE OF THE THINGS ON THE RACK.

CLAIRE, ARE YOU NEW HERE?

IT'S THAT OBVIOUS, HUH?

A LITTLE, BUT IN A GOOD WAY.

OCTAVIAN COUNTRY DAY SCHOOL
THE CAFE
12:26 P.M.
SEPTEMBER 2ND

WHAT?

I'M LOOKING AT A MINIMUM OF TWENTY POINTS FOR WHAT I'M ABOUT TO SAY.

I HAVE PLANS WITH A BRIARWOOD BOY ON SATURDAY.

67

EXCUSE ME. IS THAT A POWERSHOT S100 DIGITAL ELPH?

YEAH, I JUST GOT IT FOR MY BIRTHDAY.

THAT'S SO FUNNY, I HAVE THE EXACT SAME ONE.

ARE THOSE REAL?

NO, WE GOT THEM FROM THE DRUG-STORE.

OH, WELL, AROUND HERE YOU NEVER KNOW.

I WOULDN'T BE SURPRISED IF THOSE PICASSOS ON THE WALL WERE REAL.

THEY ARE.

MY NAME IS LAYNE.

HI, I'M CLAIRE.

AREN'T YOU MASSIE'S FRIEND?

UH, YEAH, I AM.

HOW'D YOU KNOW?

I SAW YOU WITH HER THIS MORNING. AND YOU'RE DRESSED LIKE A PURE MASSIE-CHIST.

UM, SINCE I'M NEW HERE, I'M TRYING TO MEET EVERYONE.

MASSIE WAS BUMMED ABOUT IT AT FIRST BECAUSE SHE WAS SCARED I'D MAKE OTHER FRIENDS AND DUMP HER—

SHE TOLD YOU THAT?

NOT EXACTLY. SHE WROTE IT IN AN E-MAIL.

73

75

THE GUESTHOUSE
THE LIVING ROOM
5:00 P.M.
SEPTEMBER 5TH

DID MOM TELL YOU I'M HAVING A SLEEPOVER TONIGHT?

I'M GOING OUT WITH MY NEW FRIEND LAYNE.

WAIT, HOW MANY PEOPLE ARE COMING OVER?

HOW DO YOU HAVE TWELVE FRIENDS ALREADY?

TWELVE.

THE RAISINS.

I TOLD YOU.

CLAIRE?

KENDRA?

EVERY FRIDAY NIGHT MASSIE HAS A SLEEPOVER AND I'D LIKE YOU TO COME TONIGHT.

IF YOU DON'T ALREADY HAVE PLANS.

THANKS, BUT I'M SURE MASSIE DOESN'T WANT ME AT HER PARTY.

WHO WOULD?

SHUT UP!

MASSIE INSISTS?

I INSIST.

AND MASSIE INSISTS. COME BY AT 7:30 P.M.

YES.

MASS, IT'S KRISTEN. WE'RE GOING OUT TO THE CABANA TO SET UP—YOU COMING?

GO AHEAD.

I'LL SEE YOU GUYS OUT THERE IN A BIT.

THE BLOCK ESTATE
CABANA #3
10:15 P.M.
SEPTEMBER 5TH

'KAY, WHAT WOULD YOU RATHER? A CONDITION THAT MAKES YOU SNORE 24-7 OR ONE THAT MAKES YOU FALL DOWN EVERY TEN SECONDS?

SNORE.

WHAT WOULD YOU RATHER HAVE, A LONG PIG'S TAIL, OR CHIHUAHUA EARS?

TAIL FOR ME! I ALREADY LOOK LIKE A PIG, SO I MIGHT AS WELL JUST GO WITH IT.

YOU DO NOT LOOK LIKE A PIG!

YOU JUST SMELL LIKE ONE.

93

SO WHAT IF MASSIE IS ALWAYS HAVING FUN?

SO WHAT IF THEY'RE STARTING A MAKEUP COMPANY TOGETHER?

SO WHAT IF THEY THINK I'LL NEVER BE GOOD ENOUGH FOR THEM!

IT'S THEIR LOSS!

I'M MOVING ON!

HI, CHRIS.
WAIT, LAYNE, YOUR SURNAME IS ABELEY, RIGHT?
YES, WHY?
CHRIS ABELEY!
THEEEE CHRIS ABELEY!
YOU DON'T GO TO BRIARWOOD, DO YOU?
YUP, I'M A FRESHMAN.
YES, IT'S HIM!
MY BROTHER TODD JUST STARTED IN THE MIDDLE SCHOOL.
HE'S MUCH YOUNGER THAN YOU, BUT YOU KNOW, IN CASE YOU HAPPEN TO MEET HIM.

YOUR BROTHER SEEMS REALLY NICE.

YEAH, HE'S PRETTY COOL.

YOU SHOULD SEE HOW HAPPY FAWN IS NOW THAT HE'S BACK FROM BOARDING SCHOOL.

WHO'S FAWN?

YOUR DOG?

HARDLY.

SHE'S HIS DISGUSTINGLY BEAUTIFUL GIRLFRIEND.

THEY'VE BEEN DATING SINCE SEVENTH GRADE.

108

WHAT ABOUT YOU? WHAT DO YOU LIKE DOING IN YOUR FREE TIME?

I HANG OUT WITH MY FRIENDS, LISTEN TO MUSIC, AND YOU KNOW, I LIKE ENTERTAINING WHEN MY PARENTS ARE OUT OF TOWN.

ENTERTAINING?

YOU KNOW, PARTY STUFF.

THE GUESTHOUSE
THE KITCHEN
11:11 A.M.
SEPTEMBER 13TH

SHOULDN'T LAYNE BE HERE BY NOW?

SHE'S NOT COMING.

SHE'S BUSY WITH "HER NEW" BEST FRIEND, MASSIE.

SHOULDN'T THE QUOTES BE AROUND "BEST FRIEND," DEAR?

I DON'T UNDERSTAND. CAN'T YOU ALL HANG OUT TOGETHER?

GEE, GREAT IDEA.

THE PRESIDENT COULD REALLY USE YOUR HELP WITH THAT CRISIS IN THE MIDDLE EAST.

117

118

THE BLOCK ESTATE
THE POOL
11:45 A.M.
SEPTEMBER 13TH

GLAMBITION

GLAMBITION

WHERE DO YOU THINK MASSIE IS THIS TIME?

SHE'S AN HOUR LATE.

122

BRITNEY?

WHERE WERE YOU? YOU'RE AN HOUR LATE.

I'M SO SORRY. WE RODE A NEW TRAIL AND GOT LOST. IF CHRIS WASN'T A TRAINED BOY SCOUT, WE WOULD HAVE DIED OUT THERE.

DYLAN, BE CAREFUL.

HA HA HA

HA HA HA

THOSE TARGET BATHING SUITS ARE REALLY HARD TO CLEAN.

I...

I THINK WE SHOULD LAUNCH OUR FIRST GLAMBITION PRODUCT IN A WEEK.

THE DAY THE SCHOOL GOES TO THE CITY FOR THE *ALL MY CHILDREN* TAPING.

THE GUESTHOUSE
CLAIRE'S BEDROOM
8:13 P.M.
SEPTEMBER 13TH

Massiekur: No
I'm going to hang @ Claire's. Maybe watch movies.
Luv her now! So fun!
G2G
Btw, let's wear shorts over tights monday.
Just saw it in 17. super cute!
Tell K&D
Holagurrl: Serious?
Massiekur: bout???
Holagurrl: All of it!
Massiekur: Totally. Laytah :)

136

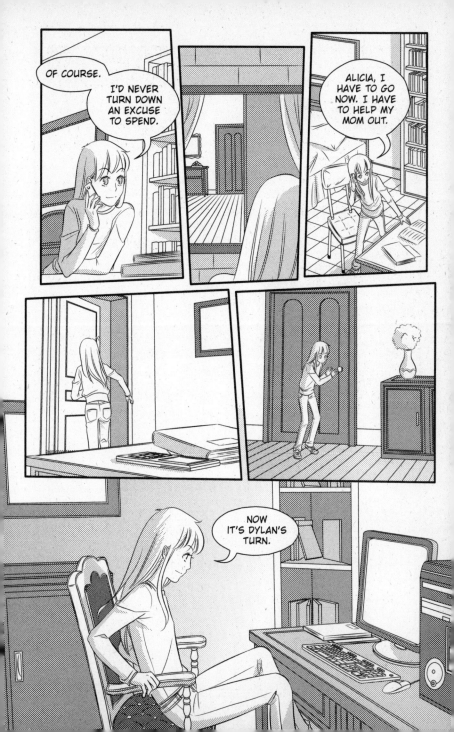

Massiekur: Whats up?
Bigredhead: Biology homework : (
Massiekur: What R U wearing to your party?
Bigredhead: Maybe a suede mini from barney's catalog, PG23
Massiekur: Think your legs will look good in a mini?
Bigredhead: Why?
Massiekur: Just asking.
G2G, claire just stopped by
Bigredhead: What, do you think I have fat legs?????????

THE BLOCK ESTATE
MASSIE'S BEDROOM
8:19 P.M.
SEPTEMBER 18TH

KRISTEN IS NEXT.

HOPE THIS'S THE LAST TIME I HAVE TO DO IT.

Massiekur:	U there?
sexysportsbabe:	Always
Massiekur:	Homework?
Sexysportsbabe:	Glambition. G 2 get an A
Massiekur:	What if U don't get 1
Sexysportsbabe:	U don't want 2 know
Massiekur:	Parents?
Sexysportsbabe:	Everything
Massiekur:	?????
Sexysportsbabe:	Forget it
Massiekur:	Tell me
Sexysportsbabe:	It's nothing

143

Massiekur: Secret 4 a secret? I have something I haven't
                 told anyone.
Sexysportsbabe: Swear?
Massiekur: Swear
Sexysportsbabe: K, U 1st
Massiekur: U know how I've been hanging out with C.A. every
                 weekend
Sexysportsbabe: Yeah, I've noticed
Massiekur: LOL
                 Layne has been with us every time
Sexysportsbabe: OMG :p
Massiekur: I've also taken her for mani/pedis and fro yo after
                 school. I actually like her
Sexysportsbabe: OMG x2

Massiekur: Your turn
Sexysportsbabe: K but you can't tell
                 U know how I'm always worried
                 about my grades? it's not just
                 cuz I have <u>strict</u> parents. it's
                 because I have <u>poor</u> parents.
Sexysportsbabe: I'm on scholarship at OCD
Massiekur: OMGx3
                 I thought your dad was a rich
                 art dealer
Sexysportsbabe: Was
Massiekur: But you live in the Montdor
                 Building!
Sexysportsbabe: Apt. building next door.
Sexysportsbabe: You better not tell! not even
                 for gossip points. K?

TIME'S UP.

Massiekur: G2G
    Massiekur has signed off 8: 30 p.m.

SHE'S PROBABLY FREAKING OUT RIGHT NOW.

WONDERING IF BY THIS TIME TOMORROW THE WHOLE SCHOOL WILL KNOW SHE'S A POSER.

GOSH, WHY DO I FEEL SO GUILTY?

THEY TOTALLY DESERVE IT, DON'T THEY?

OCTAVIAN COUNTRY DAY SCHOOL
THE LOCKER ROOM
11:40 A.M.
SEPTEMBER 20TH

WHERE'S CLAIRE?

HOW AM I SUPPOSED TO KNOW?

ISN'T SHE YOUR NEW BEST FRIEND?

146

WHERE IS EVERYONE?

DETENTION.

ALICIA'S DRIVER IS GOING TO PICK THEM UP. WE CAN GO.

Sexysportsbabe: Just 2 let U know, I have a ride for tomorrow. Don't pick me up.

Massiekur: What is going on????
Sexysportsbabe: Stop acting all innocent. I trusted you. You said you would keep our secret!!!
Massiekur: What secret? I honestly have no idea what you're talking about!

Calling... Kristen

PLEASE, PICK UP.

THE GUESTHOUSE
CLAIRE'S BEDROOM
7:45 P.M.
SEPTEMBER 20TH

HEY, DYLAN!

I HEAR YOU BOUGHT A GREAT OUTFIT FOR MY PARTY.

YEAH, IT'S PRETTY COOL.

ALICIA SAID IT LOOKED SMOKIN' ON ME. AND SHE PAID.

155

THE BLOCK ESTATE
THE DRIVEWAY
8:00 A.M.
SEPTEMBER 29TH

RING RING

CLAIRE? WHERE ARE YOU?

YOU'RE NOT MOVING OUT ALREADY, ARE YOU?

HI, ISAAC. I'M GETTING A RIDE FROM MY MOM TODAY.

WE'RE GOING TO LOOK AT A FEW HOUSES ON OUR WAY TO SCHOOL.

MAYBE.

SORRY I'M LATE.

I WAS JUST ABOUT TO CALL ABC STUDIOS AND ASK IF THEY WOULDN'T MIND TAPING *ALL MY CHILDREN* A FEW MINUTES LATER BECAUSE CLAIRE LYONS WAS RUNNING A LITTLE LATE.

BUT IF YOU CAN FIND A SEAT IN THE NEXT SECOND, I'LL REFRAIN.

172

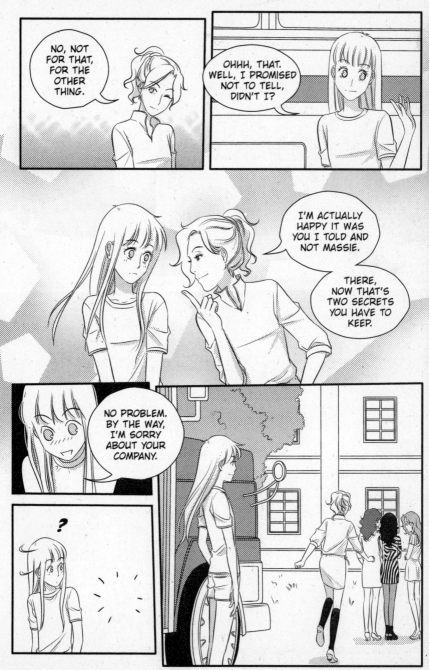

NO, NOT FOR THAT, FOR THE OTHER THING.

OHHH, THAT. WELL, I PROMISED NOT TO TELL, DIDN'T I?

I'M ACTUALLY HAPPY IT WAS YOU I TOLD AND NOT MASSIE.

THERE, NOW THAT'S TWO SECRETS YOU HAVE TO KEEP.

NO PROBLEM. BY THE WAY, I'M SORRY ABOUT YOUR COMPANY.

?

174

THE BLOCK ESTATE
MASSIE'S ROOM
7:45 P.M.
OCTOBER 3RD

MASSIE, EVERYONE IS ASKING WHERE YOU ARE.

COME ON DOWN.

'KAY.

LET'S GO BREAK SOME HEARTS, BEAN.

TAP

TAP

HI,
CHRIS.

178

YOU HAVE AN AMAZING HOUSE.
THANKS.
FAWN IS CHRIS'S GIRLFRIEND.
THEY'VE BEEN DATING SINCE THE SEVENTH GRADE.
MASSIE'S GOING TO TEACH YOU HOW TO RIDE NEXT.

183

HERE'S YOUR PRECIOUS OUTFIT AND CELL PHONE BACK.

LAYNE, DO YOU THINK YOU CAN HELP ME FIND A PART-TIME JOB?

I'VE SPENT ALL MY SAVINGS.

LAYNE?

SQUEEEAL—

SORRY ABOUT THAT, FOLKS.

193

THE END.

The greatest superpower...

...is the power to CREATE!

Watch a whole new world come to life in the manga adaptation of **James Patterson's** #1 New York Times bestselling series with art by **SeungHui Kye!**

COMING FALL 2010!

DANIEL X

Yen Press

THE CLIQUE
THE MANGA

Based on THE CLIQUE novels
written by Lisi Harrison

Art and Adaptation: Yishan Li

Lettering: Hope Donovan

Text Copyright © 2010 by Alloy Entertainment
Illustrations Copyright © 2010 by Hachette Book Group, Inc.

Yen Press
Hachette Book Group
237 Park Avenue
New York, NY 10017

www.HachetteBookGroup.com
www.YenPress.com

Yen Press is an imprint of Hachette Book Group, Inc. The Yen Press name and logo are trademarks of Hachette Book Group, Inc.

alloyentertainment
151 West 26th Street, New York, NY 10001
alloyentertainment.com

First Yen Press Edition: July 2010

ISBN: 978-0-7595-3029-4

10 9 8 7 6 5 4 3 2 1

CW

Printed in the United States of America